For Sarah, the first and for her first
—E.B.

For Théophile
—PHB

First published in France under the title *Les Premières Fois* © 1999 Editions du Seuil

English language translation © 2000 Stewart, Tabori & Chang

Published in 2000 by
Stewart, Tabori & Chang
A division of U.S. Media Holdings, Inc.
115 West 18th Street
New York, NY 10011

Distributed in Canada by
General Publishing Company Ltd.
30 Lesmill Road
Don Mills, Ontario, Canada M3B 2T6

Library of Congress Cataloging-in-Publication Data
Brami, Elisabeth.
[Premières fois. English]
First times/ Elisabeth Brami & Philippe Bertrand;
translated by Siobhán McGowan.
p. cm.
ISBN 1-58479-019-9 (hardcover)
1. Children—Miscellanea—Juvenile literature. I. Bertrand,
Philippe, 1949- II. McGowan, Siobhán. III. Title.
HQ781.B7313 2000
305.23—dc21   99-058058

Printed in Belgium

10 9 8 7 6 5 4 3 2 1

First Printing

FIRST TIMES

ÉLISABETH BRAMI

PHILIPPE BERTRAND

Translated by Siobhán McGowan

Stewart, Tabori & Chang
New York

The first day
of classes ...

... your legs felt like molasses.

The
first time
you had
a crush ...

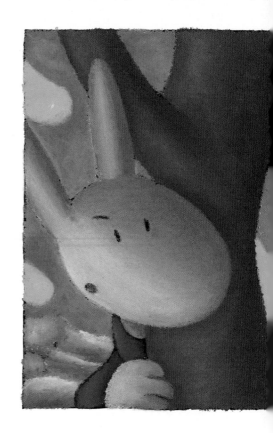

... it was really serious.

The first time

you rode your

bike without

the training wheels ...

... at a few of the corners,

you braked with your heels.

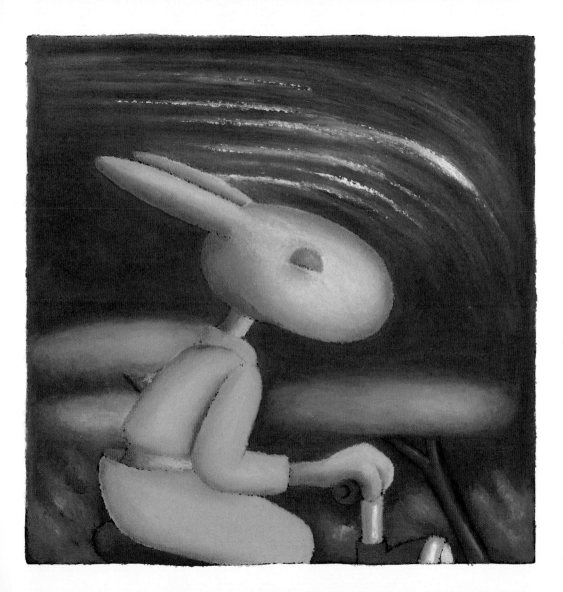

The first time
you saw your
newborn sister
or brother ...

... you wanted to send baby back,
but didn't tell your mother.

The first time

you used a

phone to talk

to a friend ...

... Amazing!
There was
someone
on the
other end!

The first time

you threw

a party—

vroom, vroom!

... you pushed all the furniture
to the back of the room.

The first time

you put on

nail polish,

even painted

your toes ...

... you felt glamorous as a movie star,
and struck a Hollywood pose.

The first time

you were

punished for a

very big mistake ...

... you cried for a hug and a kiss,
and it kept you awake.

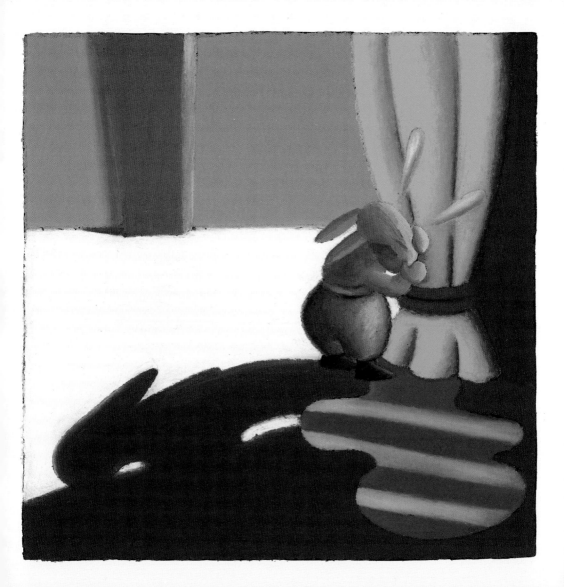

The first time

you went

to camp for

summer vacation ...

... you thought you might cry, when you said good-bye,
to your mom and dad at the train station.

The first time

you read all

the words

in a book ...

... you still
used your
finger to help
you look.

The first time

you received

a letter

in the mail ...

... you ripped it right open, tooth and nail.

The first time

you walked

home from

school after dark ...

... the house seemed so far away:
no stopping in the park!

The first time

you needed

medical aid ...

... at the hospital, you were afraid.

The first time

you had

a little

pocket money ...

... you bought things that were kind of funny.

The first time

you caught lice ...

... it wasn't very nice—
you scratched at your neck,
used a mirror to check—
and your mom was a wreck.

The first time

you cursed

in front of

your parents ...

... you felt oddly content,

but feared punishment.

The first time
you stayed up 'til
the crack of dawn ...

... you ended up sleeping the whole day long.

The first time

someone

you knew

"passed on" ...

... you wondered where the body had gone.

The first time
you moved,
instead of risking
the van ...

... you carried your
most prized possessions by hand.

The first time

you owned

a pet ...

... like a good parent,
you took it to the vet.

The first time

you were no

longer afraid

of the dark ...

... you slept tight,

through the night, without the hall light.

The first time

you sat in

a theater or

concert hall ...

... you clapped when

the lights came up

for the curtain call.

The first time

you were taken

to the barbershop ...

... when it was all over,
your hair had been chopped.

The first time

you saw the ocean's tide ...

... you searched to see land on the other side.

The first time

you were given

an unfair

punishment ...

... you protested to your parents
that you were innocent.

The first time you

were ignored by kids

in the neighborhood ...

... the reason was something you never understood.

The first time

you watched as a

grown-up cried ...

... you'd have said something nice,
but were too surprised.

The first time

you bought a gift,

you made the

salesman smile ...

... when you broke your piggy bank
and stacked your coins in a pile.

The first time
you were able to sleep
without sucking
your thumb or
clutching your blanket
for security ...

... you announced it to the whole family (though sometimes you still did both, secretly)...

The first time

you buried a

dead animal ...

... you cried a lot—that's only normal.

The first time
you lost a
baby tooth,
after the
tooth fairy
paid a visit ...

... you started to fiddle
with the tooth next to it.

The first time

you had your

picture taken in

one of those instant

photo places ...

... you laughed
at the camera and
made silly faces!

The first time

you went

to the movies ...

... Impossible! It was even better than TV.

The first time

you hurt

someone

by accident ...

... well, it wasn't your finest moment.

The first time

you wrote your

name on the wall ...

... soapy scrub-brushes
wouldn't erase it all.

The first time

you packed

your new

backpack

for school ...

... you were so upset

the night before, you almost lost your cool.

The first time

you got lost

in a store,

at the beach

or the zoo ...

... actually... how old were you?

The first time
you realized
that grown-ups
lie, too ...

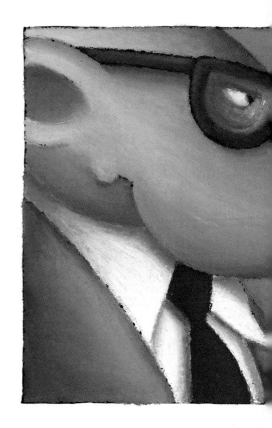

... you wondered if it was still wrong to do.

The first time

you flew in a plane

(in case you've forgotten) ...

... it was as if you were

walking on clouds made of cotton.

The first time

you wrote

the new date:

two thousand ...

... you realized time

doesn't stop, it slips by like sand.